CLASSICS
Playalong *for* Clarinet

WISE PUBLICATIONS
London/New York/Paris/Sydney/Copenhagen/Madrid

Music Sales Limited
8/9 Frith Street, London W1V 5TZ, England.
Music Sales Corporation
257 Park Avenue South, New York, NY10010, USA.
Music Sales Pty Limited
120 Rothschild Avenue, Rosebery, NSW 2018, Australia.

Order No. AM955537
ISBN 0-7119-7359-8
This book © Copyright 1999 by Wise Publications.

Book design by Michael Bell Design.
Music arranged by Paul Honey.
Music processed by Enigma Music Production Services.
Cover photography by George Taylor.
Printed in the United Kingdom by Page Bros., Norwich, Norfolk.

CD produced by Paul Honey.
Instrumental solos by John Whelan & Jamie Talbot.
Engineered by Kester Sims.

Your Guarantee of Quality:
As publishers, we strive to produce every book to
the highest commercial standards.
The music has been freshly engraved and the book has been
carefully designed to minimise awkward page turns and
to make playing from it a real pleasure.
Particular care has been given to specifying acid-free, neutral-sized
paper made from pulps which have not been elemental chlorine bleached.
This pulp is from farmed sustainable forests and was
produced with special regard for the environment.
Throughout, the printing and binding have been planned to
ensure a sturdy, attractive publication which should give years of enjoyment.
If your copy fails to meet our high standards,
please inform us and we will gladly replace it.

Music Sales' complete catalogue describes thousands of
titles and is available in full colour sections by subject,
direct from Music Sales Limited.
Please state your areas of interest and send a
cheque/postal order for £1.50 for postage to:
Music Sales Limited, Newmarket Road, Bury St. Edmunds, Suffolk IP33 3YB.

Clarinet Fingering Chart

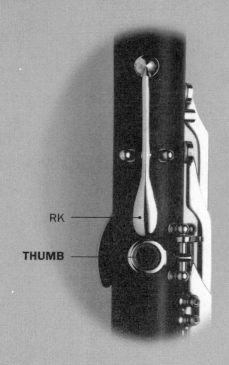

RK

THUMB

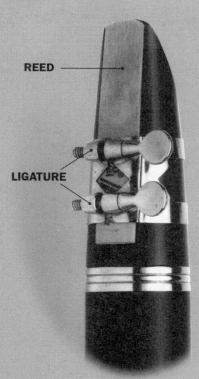

REED

LIGATURE

Mouthpiece

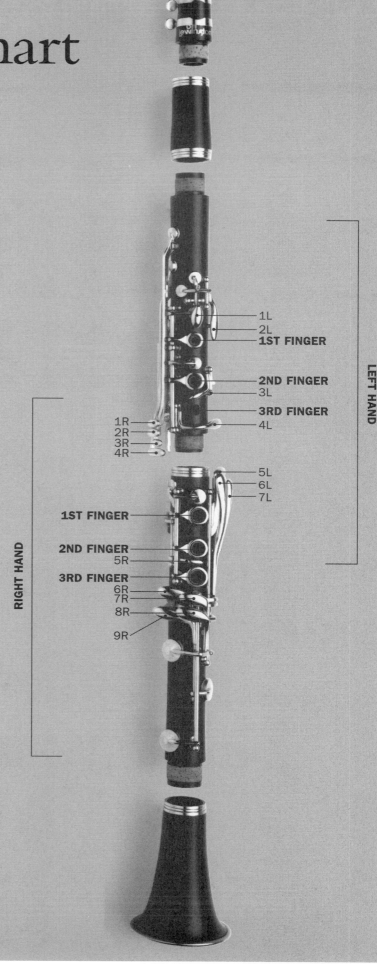

LEFT HAND

1L
2L
1ST FINGER

2ND FINGER
3L

3RD FINGER
4L

1R
2R
3R
4R

5L
6L
7L

RIGHT HAND

1ST FINGER

2ND FINGER
5R

3RD FINGER
6R
7R
8R

9R

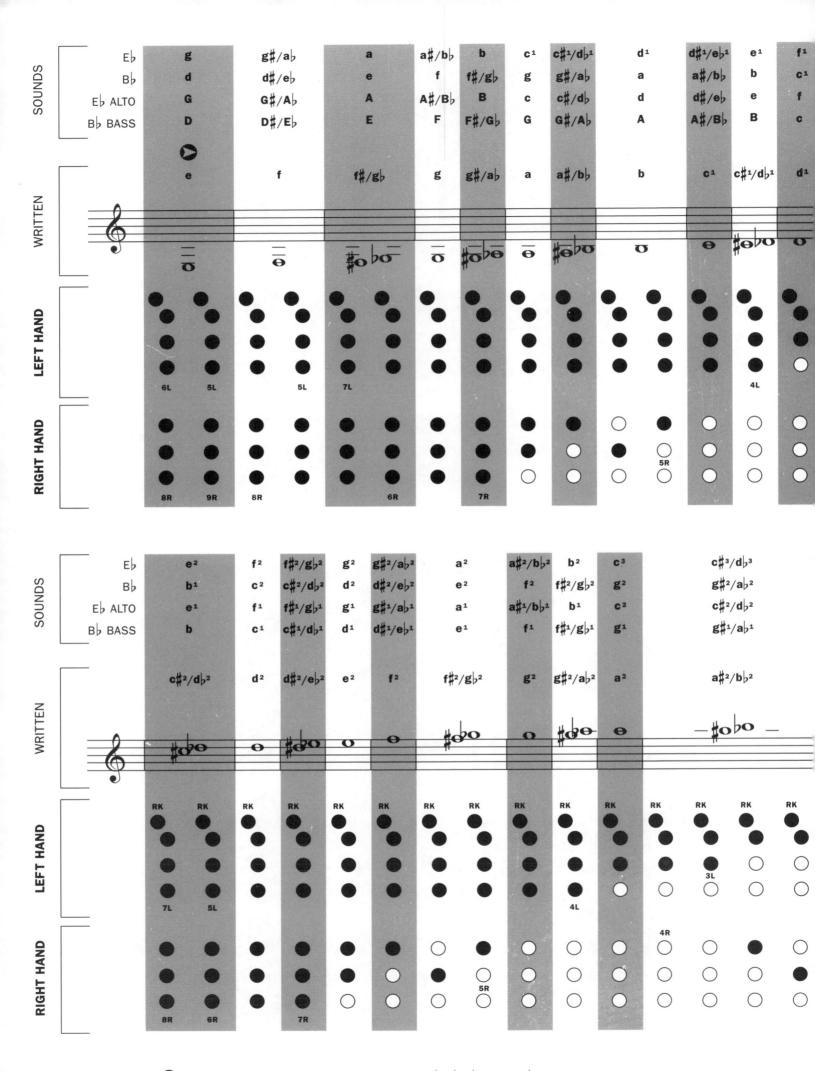

Indicates the lower limit of the best playing range for E♭, B♭, E♭ Alto and B♭ Bass Clarinets

Indicates the upper limit of the best playing range for E♭ and B♭ Clarinets

Indicates the upper limit of the best playing range for E♭ Alto and B♭ Bass Clarinets

Ave Maria

Based on Bach's Prelude No.1 in C Major

Composed by Charles Gounod

Andante

Air On The 'G' String

Composed by Johann Sebastian Bach

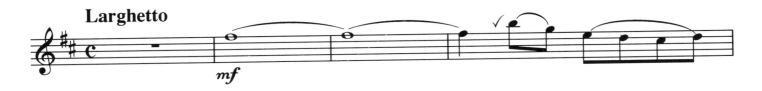

Habañera

from Carmen

Composed by Georges Bizet

Andantino

14

Jupiter
from The Planets Suite

Composed by Gustav Holst

Andante maestoso

New World Symphony

Theme

Composed by Antonin Dvořák

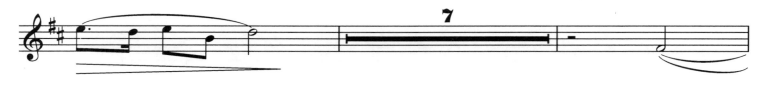

Ode To Joy
Theme from Symphony No.9 'Choral'

Composed by Ludwig van Beethoven

Allegro

Rondo in D Minor

from Abdelazer

Composed by Henry Purcell
As used in Young Person's Guide To The Orchestra - Britten

poco rall.

Swan Lake

Theme

Composed by Peter Ilyich Tchaikovsky

Spring

from The Four Seasons

Composed by Antonio Vivaldi

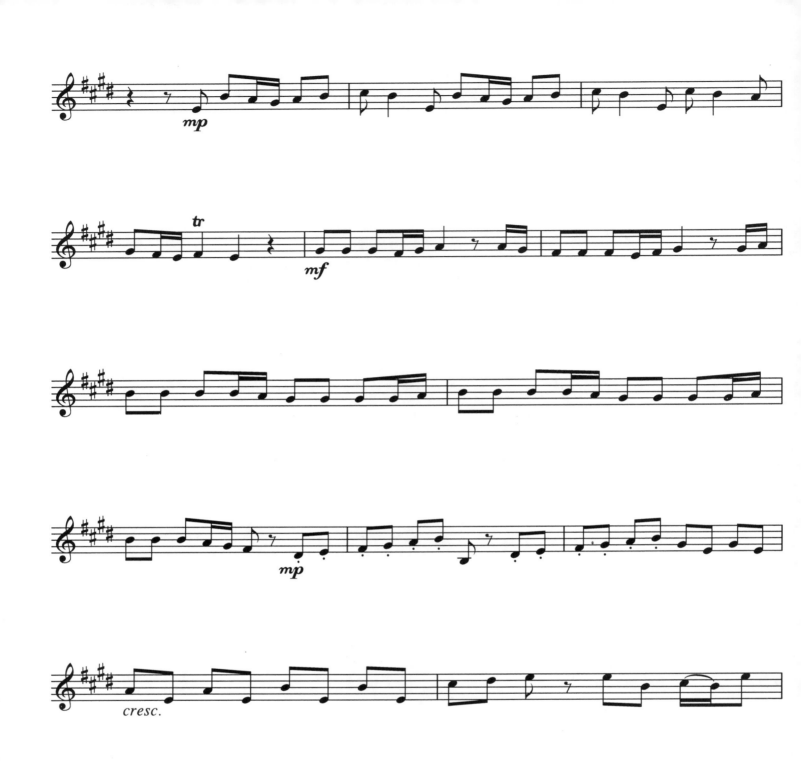

Hornpipe
from The Water Music

Composed by George Frideric Handel

Allegro

f non legato

3/00 (36838)